Seconds

Seconds

Bryan Lee O'Malley

with

Jason Fischer . . . . Drawing Assistant

Dustin Harbin . . . . Lettering

Nathan Fairbairn . . . . Color

RANDOM HOUSE CANADA

PUBLISHED BY RANDOM HOUSE CANADA

Copyright © 2014 Bryan Lee O'Malley

www.randomhouse.ca

Random House Canada and colophon are registered trademarks.

Grateful acknowledgment is made to Hal Leonard Corporation for permission to reprint an excerpt from "Over and Over" words and music by Christine McVie, copyright © 1979 by Universal Music-Careers. International copyright secured. All rights reserved. Reprinted by permission of Hal Leonard Corporation.

Library and Archives Canada Cataloguing in Publication

O'Malley, Bryan Lee, author, illustrator
Seconds / Bryan Lee O'Malley.

Issued in print and electronic formats.

ISBN 978-0-307-36306-0
eBook ISBN 978-0-307-36307-7

1. Graphic novels. I. Title.

PN6733.043S43 2014   741.5'971   C2013-906409-5

Printed and bound in China

10 9 8 7 6 5 4 3 2 1

I felt a kind of vertigo, as if
I were merely plunging from
one world to another, and in
each I arrived shortly after
the end of the world had
taken place

—Italo Calvino,
If on a winter's night a traveler

And I said
Could it be me?
Could it really, really be?
Over and over

—Fleetwood Mac

Seconds

She
woke
up,

and
there
was a
glow.

She made a conscious decision not to freak out.

After all, she was clearly dreaming.

AWAKE?

If she were awake, she maybe would have noticed this decrepit room, the rotten blanket, the bare bulb.

AWAKE NOW?

WHO ARE YOU?

Only the dresser was familiar.

SHFF

Or at least

SHFFF

it had been.

There was nothing inside.

Not even socks.

She woke up the next morning remembering none of this.

9

1

Katie

Katie was stressed out.

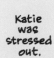 I'M PERFECTLY FINE.

She was sleeping too little, worrying too much, feeling old.

 SHE WAS IN HER TWENTIES AND YOUNG AND TOTALLY GREAT.

At 29, she felt like everything was slipping away.

 UM, NO.

...and she was talking to herself more than usual.

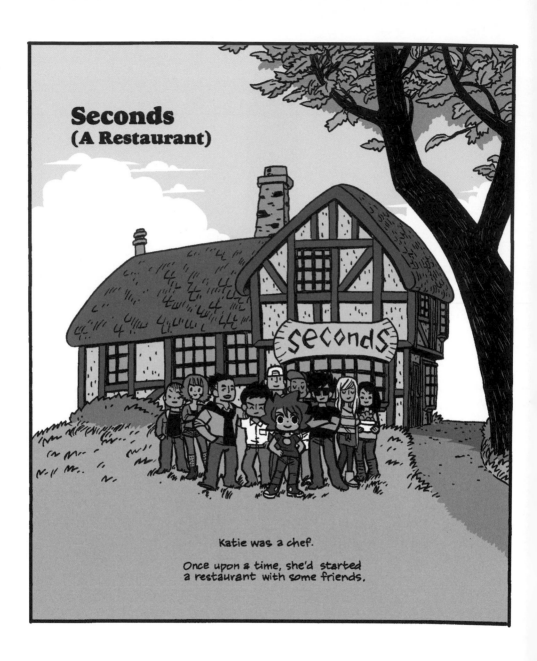

Seconds
(A Restaurant)

Katie was a chef.

Once upon a time, she'd started
a restaurant with some friends.

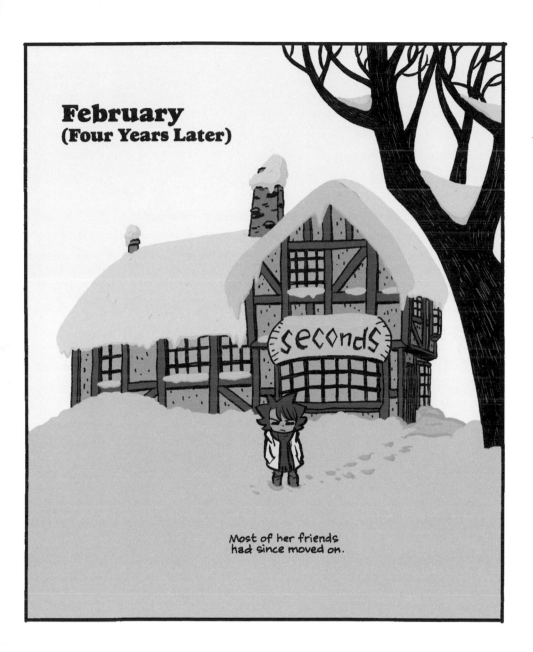

February
(Four Years Later)

seconds

Most of her friends
had since moved on.

It was still good. She was still proud of it.

WELCOME TO SECONDS OH IT'S YOU *NEVER MIND THEN*

But she was four years older now, and everyone around her seemed infinitely younger.

The original staff were all gone. The new kids were like a bunch of stylish, sullen babies.

For this and a billion other reasons, Katie was starting a new restaurant.

22 Lucknow Street
(across the river)

Ancient, decrepit, the building had been empty since she was a kid.

It was falling apart, but there'd always been something magical about it all the same.

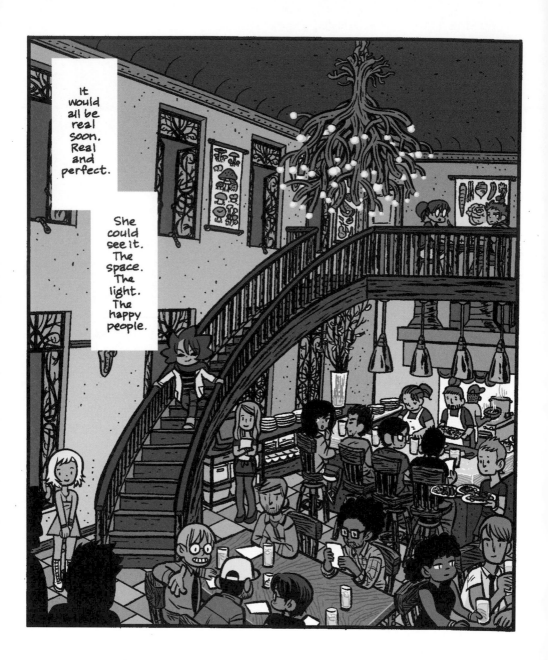

It would all be real soon. Real and perfect.

She could see it. The space. The light. The happy people.

But right now the space was all insulation and exposed pipes.

The light was filled with sawdust.

Instead of happy diners she had boring construction dudes.

It wasn't a restaurant yet.

It wasn't anything yet.

I THINK THIS IS ALL GOING REALLY WELL.

THE HELL IT IS.

OKAY, OKAY, IT ISN'T GOING WELL. BUT IT ISN'T GOING *POORLY!*

Arthur
Katie's new business partner (34 years old)

I'M TOLD OUR PERMITS ARE DONE, SO THE GUYS ARE ABOUT TO--

DUDE, THIS SUCKS! IT'S TAKING *FOREVER!* WHAT AM I SUPPOSED TO DO?!

KATIE, HOW LONG HAVE YOU BEEN WAITING FOR THIS?

I DUNNO. LIKE FOUR YEARS OR *MY ENTIRE LIFE,* DEPENDING WHERE YOU START COUNTING FROM.

SO WHAT'S A *MONTH?* ANYWAY, AS I WAS--

KATIE.

HM?

phone

OH HEY, I THOUGHT OF A NAME.

FANTASTIC! HIT ME WITH IT. WOW ME. FIRST CUSTOMER RIGHT HERE.

UH,... "KATIE'S."

. . .

WHAT?! IT FITS ON THE SIGN AND EVERYTHING!

I'M JUST AMAZED THAT YOU CAME UP WITH IT ALL BY YOURSELF.

HA HA.

ANYWAY, IT'S YOUR RESTAURANT. YOU'RE THE BOSS AND YOU'RE THE GENIUS, SO WHY NOT HAVE YOUR NAME ON THE SIGN?

IT'S A BOLD MOVE FOR A BOLD PLACE.

YOU ARE *SUCH* A SUCK-UP!

Not that she minded.

19

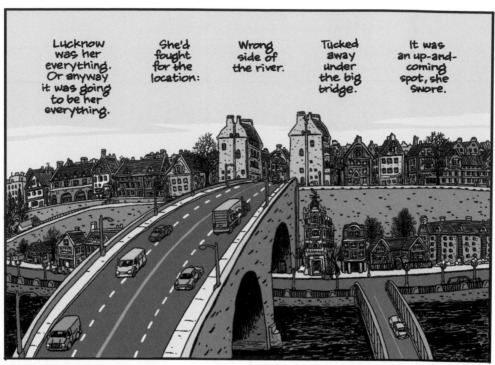

Lucknow was her everything. Or anyway it was going to be her everything.

She'd fought for the location:

Wrong side of the river.

Tucked away under the big bridge.

It was an up-and-coming spot, she swore.

She drove back and forth sometimes four, five times a day.

As if one of these times she'd cross that little bridge and find a finished restaurant.

The waiting was hell.

Seconds had become her purgatory.

At least purgatory had its perks.

PARK

21

Max
Katie's ex(?!)

Max was here.

Max was back.

Max smiled.

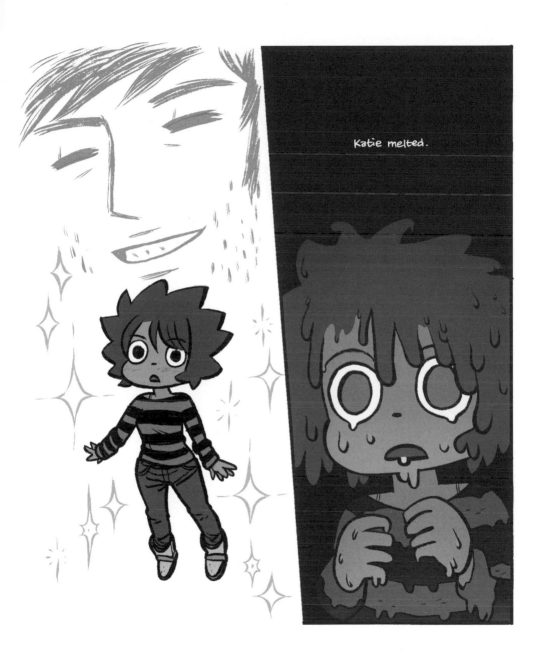

Katie melted.

Then, slowly, stupidly, she realized that Max was with a girl.

A girl who was preposterously lovely.

And she remembered that he'd left for a reason.

WOW. I GUESS THIS MAKES IT OFFICIAL.

UHH... KATIE, YOU REMEMBER MATILDA.

YOUR SISTER? COME ON. SHE'S LIKE TWELVE.

(DEEPLY UNCOMFORTABLE)

I'M ACTUALLY NINETEEN NOW. HI.

WHAT. NO.

SO, KATIE, UM, IF YOU HAVE A MINUTE, MAYBE WE COULD--

SORRY, BRO, THEY NEED ME DOWN-STAIRS.

I'LL LEAVE YOU IN THE CAPABLE HANDS OF... UH...

HAZEL.

I KNOW YOUR NAME!

← bad boss

KATIE... GIVE ME A CHANCE HERE.

I'M LITERALLY TOO BUSY TO KEEP TALKING.

TIME IS MONEY, MAX!

OH PLEASE!

Katie was an idiot.

WHAT? NO. THAT WAS SO SMOOTH.

Was that really his sister?

Had so much time passed?

WHO EVEN CARES? NOT ME.

27

Seconds was in an old building, and most of the magic happened down in the basement (purely out of necessity).

For four years she'd dreamed of a bright, airy kitchen, and at Lucknow she'd finally get it.

She really couldn't wait.

SO WHY ARE YOU STILL HERE, KATIE?

Raymond
Co-owner
of Seconds

Ray and his boyfriend had put up all the money four years ago.

They'd rolled the dice on Katie's cooking.

Now they owned the best restaurant in town.

And she didn't.

BEST
of the city

"SECONDS"
Best Dinner Spot
3 YEARS
IN A ROW!

So she'd been saving every penny. Living in the same crummy apartment, driving the same crummy car, biding her time.

And she'd done it.

At Lucknow Katie would be an equal partner. Just the thought of it energized her.

(Katie's dorky imagination)

BUT IT'S TAKING SOOO MUCH LONGER THAN I EVER IMAGINED.

AND I JUST WANNA *COOOOK!*

SO *COOK.* YOU'RE THE ONE WHO INSISTED ON LEAVING.

I DON'T WANNA COOK *HERE!* *CHOKED SOB*

THREE MONTHS TRAINING THE NEW GUY AND SCALING YOUR HOURS BACK BIT BY BIT. FINALLY WE'RE PHASING YOUR ASS OUT. YET HERE YOU ARE.

YOU KNOW YOU'RE JUST GETTING IN THE WAY NOW, RIGHT?

OFTEN LITERALLY.

MOAANNN

IMPORTANT PAPERWORK!

She wasn't chef anymore, or kitchen manager, or really anything. But she still acted like the boss, and the new babies at Seconds treated her accordingly.

She'd hand-picked her successor.

Plucked him from obscurity.

He was young, talented, hard-working. He could have been her protégé. Instead he was... not.

Chef Andrew
(25 years old)

AND WHAT DO WE HAVE HERE?

OH. IT'S GARBAGE.

THIS IS GARBAGE TOO.

YEP... THIS IS ALSO GARBAGE.

HMM THIS IS ALMOST-- OOPS, NO, SORRY, IT'S GARBAGE.

WOW, DUDE.

STARE

TURN THAT RIDICULOUS ASS RIGHT AROUND AND GET THE HELL OUT OF MY KITCHEN BEFORE I *THROW* YOU OUT.

OOH, LOOK AT THE BIG MAN! IT'S *YOUR* KITCHEN NOW? I *BUILT* THIS KITCHEN, BUDDY!

YEAH, AND THEN YOU PUT *ME* IN CHARGE OF IT. YOU OUGHTA KNOW BETTER THAN COME IN HERE AND ACT LIKE YOU DIDN'T.

ANDY, BABY, DON'T GET ME WRONG. I'VE GOT A *TON* OF RESPECT FOR YOUR WORK.

YO! ARE YOU *TOUCHING MY GARNISH?!*

MAYBE I AM! WHAT ARE YOU GONNA *DO* ABOUT IT, *HUH?!*

34

Hazel
(21 years old)

37

Apparently what had happened was this:

UMM, LIKE, I GUESS SHE CAME IN TO GET THE PARSLEY?

Patrick
Line cook
(22 years old)

SOMEONE (ANDREW) LEFT IT OVER HERE.

ANDREW'S STATION

BUT IT SHOULD BE HERE.

SERVER STATION

AND HAZEL, Y'KNOW, SHE'S SO SKINNY AND QUIET, SHE MUST HAVE SLIPPED IN...

SHE PROBABLY JUST DIDN'T WANT TO BOTHER ME.

I WAS LIKE JUST ABOUT TO ASK HER OUT, TOO... WOULDA BEEN TOMORROW...

YOU'VE BEEN SAYING THAT SINCE HER FIRST DAY, DUDE.

They kept Hazel overnight at the hospital (mostly, the doctor said, because she kept fainting at the sight of herself).

Katie had distracted Andrew from his kitchen.

She'd as good as caused the accident.

They both had.

SO *THIS* IS OVER.

NO SHIT THIS IS OVER.

GO HOME, KATIE.

Going home was easy; she lived two floors up. She'd been renting the tiny upstairs apartment from Ray for the past four years.

It must have been three in the morning.

Secon

scroll
scroll
scroll

TOSS

How
could
things

have
gone
so
wrong?

SHFF

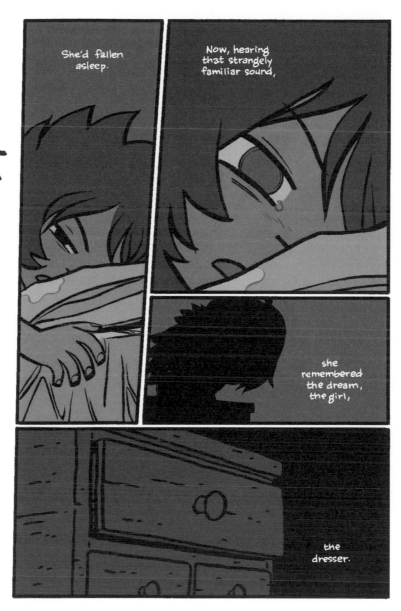

She'd fallen asleep.

Now, hearing that strangely familiar sound,

she remembered the dream, the girl,

the dresser.

It had been there when she moved in.

Maybe it had always been there.

She used it every day, but tonight it was an alien object.

It was empty, like before.

But when she searched one last time,

KLK

? ?
? ? ?

she found the hidden panel, and the little box behind it.

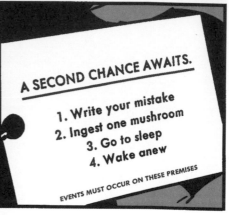

A SECOND CHANCE AWAITS.

1. Write your mistake
2. Ingest one mushroom
3. Go to sleep
4. Wake anew

EVENTS MUST OCCUR ON THESE PREMISES

Contents of the little box:

notebook titled "MY MISTAKES"

one (1) mysterious red-capped mushroom

immaculately printed instruction card

FLIP

The notebook felt old, like something from an earlier era.

Judging by the heft of it, some of its pages had been removed at some point in the past.

She'd need a pen. And one was there.

SNIC

Her favorite pen. So familiar in her hand. She hadn't seen it since the third day of high school.

My Mistake
by Katie Clay
I shouldn't of fooled around W/ ANDREW! Workplace canoodling is NO GOOD!

FLIP

MY MISTAKES

47

REVISION #1

She woke up,

and something had changed.

2
Hazel

That morning, the girl wasn't at the hospital.

Katie found the girl's address in a three-month-old unread work email (re: new staff).

HAZEL.

HER NAME'S HAZEL.

53

55

Katie's heart wouldn't stop racing.

Was her memory meaningless? Her experience insubstantial?

Was she losing her grip on reality?

Was she even awake?

HEY.

THERE SHE IS.

WHAT UP, K?

HEY, BOSS.

HEY.

DO YOU REMEMBER LAST NIGHT?

NOTHING PARTICULARLY STANDS OUT, BUT YEAH, I RECALL THAT IT TOOK PLACE.

I MEAN, DO YOU REMEMBER WHEN WE ARGUED AND THEN CAME IN HERE AND MADE OUT?

KATIE.

NONE OF THAT SHIT HAPPENED LAST NIGHT.

WHAT *DID* HAPPEN LAST NIGHT?

YOU CAME IN THE KITCHEN ALL SAYING NICE THINGS INSTEAD OF BEING A CRAZY BITCH.

SO *HA,* YA GOT ME.

So, to recap:

Katie ate a mushroom that she'd found in her dresser drawer in the middle of the night

and either she was losing her mind

or she'd changed the universe.

But

something HAD changed.

THE ACCIDENT **DID** HAPPEN. I **KNOW** IT DID.

The sickening smell of it

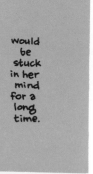

would be stuck in her mind for a long time.

And if the smell was real, the accident was real.

Hazel had burned,

and then she hadn't.

It had been Katie's fault.

BUT NOW IT'S NO-ONE'S FAULT!

Katie had *fixed* it.

She had been given a second chance.

And it seemed like she was the only one who knew.

60

After that, Katie couldn't think of anything better to do with her evening than stalk Hazel.

She quickly realized that Hazel was probably universally hated for the following reasons:

(1) She was way too tall and pretty.

(SHORT)

(2) Her hair was, like, so nice.

(3) Despite being a total fox, she acted like a shy little kid.

HAZEL? UM, YEAH.

IT'S BEEN LIKE THREE MONTHS AND THE OTHER SERVERS HAVEN'T REALLY, UH, WARMED TO HER.

WIPE

IS SHE WEIRD?

SURE. A LITTLE. MAYBE.

HAZEL? OH *MAN.* DON'T EVEN GET ME STARTED.

There was no need to get Yana started; she was already off.

SHE GETS *SO* EMBARASSED BY LIKE ANY HARMLESS COMMENT.

IT'S LIKE COME *ON,* HAZEL, I'M A SUPER-NICE PERSON.

I THINK SHE'S LIKE *OCD* OR SOMETHING.

SHE'S SUPER INTO SWEEPING AND CLEANING.

I MEAN, YES, IT'S PART OF THE JOB, BUT THIS IS ABOVE AND BEYOND.

SHE'S ESPECIALLY WEIRD ABOUT THE FIREPLACE.

AND...

SHE LEAVES FOOD OUT AT THE END OF THE NIGHT.

LIKE, *INTENTIONALLY!* IT'S SENSELESS! WHY EVEN CLEAN?

MAYBE SHE LOVES RATS? LIKE SHE COMMUNICATES WITH ANIMALS OR SOMETHING? SHE SURE DOESN'T LIKE *HUMANS.*

SO YOU THINK WE SHOULD LET HER GO?

NO! ARE YOU *KIDDING?* THAT GIRL MAKES ME LOOK *SO GOOD.*

KSHH
KSHH
KSHH

I ADMIRE THAT KIND OF DEDICATION.

65

ALIVE?

IS IT A RAT?

IT ISN'T REAL.

I MEAN, IT'S A METAPHOR. I REALIZE THAT.

BUT I LIKE THE IDEA OF IT.

Clothes, neatly folded.

WE MAKE THINGS GOOD FOR THEM... THEY MAKE THINGS GOOD FOR US.

IT'S SO SIMPLE.

ANYWAY, I TRY AND DO THINGS BY THE BOOK AROUND HERE.

And... the clothes went on the mantel.

This girl really was weird.

THERE'S A BOOK? ...CAN I BORROW IT?

NO NO NO NO NO, THERE IS NO ACTUAL BOOK.

YEAH, I GOT THAT. "BY THE BOOK." FIGURE OF SPEECH. I WAS JOKING.

OH.

The next morning,

the fire was still flickering,

and Hazel's clothes

weren't there.

3
Lis

It felt like she hadn't seen Arthur in a week, which was unusual.

HEY.

WHERE AAARE YOU, DUDE?

I TOLD YOU LIKE FIFTY TIMES.

I KNOW. SORRY. BRAIN BAD.

She suddenly remembered, but only after it was too late.

...FUNERAL.

I... UM... I'M SORRY FOR YOUR... I MEAN... YOU KNOW...

IT IS WHAT IT IS, KATIE. ENOUGH ABOUT ME. I'M FINE. ARE YOU ALRIGHT?

OH... SURE... YEAH. THINGS ARE OKAY...

GREAT. LISTEN, JUST LEAVE THE SITE TO ME, KATIE. EVERYTHING'S FINE. THERE'S NOTHING TO GET ALARMED ABOUT. I'M TAKING CARE OF IT.

HEY, ARTHUR, GUESS WHERE I'M PARKED?

HINT: IT STILL HASN'T SOLD.

DAMN IT, KATIE, TALMADGE AGAIN? STOP DOING THIS TO YOURSELF.

WE MADE OUR CHOICE AND IT'S GOING TO WORK OUT FINE. DON'T WALLOW.

771 Talmadge Street

She decided she'd spend the day cooking. It'd keep her busy, calm her nerves, and give her something to show off about later.

At the market, Katie found herself buying like a bushel of mushrooms-- she'd been craving them. On the drive back to Seconds she came up with the dish.

HSSSSSH

SHKK

She'd made all of it before, but today it came together into a dish she knew was working.

74

It was pretty pathetic.

SHUT UP. I KNOW. ≥Sniff≤

She sat there heaving and trying to make herself cry.

THAT'S NOT EVEN WHAT I'M--

CAN I JUST HAVE A MOMENT TO MYSELF?

The saddest thing was that she couldn't have a moment away from herself.

And then

through a crack in the floorboards.

she saw

something.

the girl was there.

Had she drifted off in the bath? This didn't *feel* like a dream.

Katie honestly couldn't tell anymore.

The girl was all gangly limbs,

ghostly white hair,

too many layers.

Was she even real?

ARE YOU REAL?

IS THIS EVEN HAPPENING?

?

The girl didn't even act like a person.

More like a cat, or a bird.

WHAT ABOUT A NAME? DO YOU HAVE A NAME?

MY NAME IS KATIE.

YES.

KNOW THIS.

OKAY, STALKER. AND *YOUR* NAME IS....?

LIS.

LIS?

THAT'S YOUR NAME? LIS?

I WANT YOU TO GO, LIS. YOU DON'T LIVE HERE, OKAY?

THERE ARE PLACES OUT THERE WHERE YOU CAN GET THE HELP THAT YOU CLEARLY NEED.

YOU SHOULD GO TO ONE OF THEM.

SECONDS IS A *RESTAURANT*, NOT A...

...CHARITY.

Lis was gone. And as a parting gift, she'd rearranged all of Katie's furniture.

WHERE'D SHE COME FROM? WHY'S SHE ALWAYS HANGING AROUND?

IS SHE YOUR FRIEND? WHAT ARE YOU GUYS, ART STUDENTS OR SOMETHING?

IS THIS SOME KIND OF AVANT-GARDE PRANK?

I...

I MADE HER UP.

IT'S SUPPOSED TO BE THE HOUSE SPIRIT...

IT'S JUST A DRAWING. I MAKE STUFF UP.

IT ISN'T REAL...

92

THERE! YOU SEE?

SEE WHAT?

??? ???

I DON'T SEE *ANYTHING.*

IS THIS A PRACTICAL JOKE? BECAUSE... I'M VERY GULLIBLE.

GIVE MUSH-ROOM.

ARE YOU KIDDING ME? NO!

PUT MY SHIT BACK WHERE IT BELONGS FIRST!

PUT MY STUFF *BACK,* LIS!!

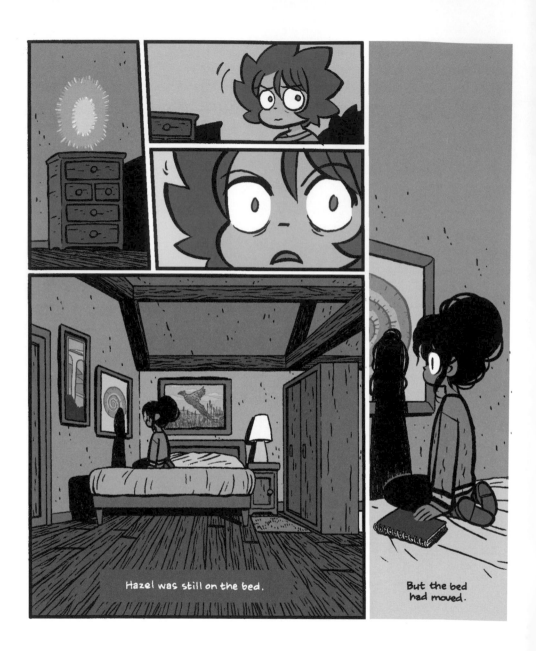

Hazel was still on the bed.

But the bed had moved.

IN THE BACK OF MY MIND I KNEW SOMEONE WAS PROBABLY JUST TAKING MY STUFF. I'M NOT AN IDIOT.

BUT I THINK PART OF ME ALWAYS WANTED TO BELIEVE SHE WAS REAL.

HAZEL. I'VE SEEN HER LIKE FOUR TIMES.

SHE'S DEFINITELY REAL.

SO WHY CAN'T YOU SEE HER?

SIP

REMEMBER WHEN YOU SAID YOU DO THINGS BY THE BOOK, AND I KNEW IT WAS A FIGURE OF SPEECH, AND WE ALL LAUGHED?

UM... YEAH?

I SECRETLY THOUGHT THERE REALLY WAS A BOOK AND NOW I WISH IT WERE TRUE.

...WELL...

...IN MY GRANDMA'S STORIES, THE HOUSE SPIRIT WOULD ALWAYS APPEAR TO THE MASTER OF THE HOUSE.

WHO'S THAT?

WHOEVER'S IN CHARGE? LIKE, UM, THE PATRIARCH, USUALLY...

...OR THE BOSS.

HEY, RAY, YOU'RE THE BOSS AT SECONDS, RIGHT?

I MEAN YOU'RE IN CHARGE?

ME... IN CHARGE...?

WELL, HUH...

MAYBE WHEN YOU GET YOUR NEW RESTAURANT GOING...

OR WHEN YOU STOP LIVING HERE.

OR, LIKE... IF YOU *DIED*.

OR... IN BUDDHISM THERE'S A MEASURE OF TIME CALLED A *KALPA* -- IT'S LIKE SIXTEEN MILLION YEARS--

GREAT. THANKS.

YO. BOSS. WANT ME TO MAKE YOU SOME DINNER BEFORE THE RUSH?

PLEASE STOP CALLING ME THAT.

CALLING YOU WHAT? BOSS?

YES.

OK, BOSS.

OK, BOSS?

She stepped out for some air, then found herself making an unplanned excursion.

FAST EDDY BURGER

A long time ago, this had been her favorite restaurant.

DOUBLE CHEESE-BURGER. EXTRA ONIONS, EXTRA MAYO. HOT SAUCE. NO FRIES. WAIT. YES FRIES.

HM, ARE YOU TELLING ME A SECRET? SPEAK UP, PLEASE.

Before she'd started cooking, before her mom had gotten sick, everything had been this easy.

It was like eating an old friend.

CHOMP
CHOMP
CHOMP
URP

Katie decided some serious ego-stroking would cap off her evening perfectly.

DOCTOR AND MRS. ANDRETTI! HOW ARE WE DOING TONIGHT?

VERY WELL, THANK YOU, KATIE.

I GOTTA TELL YOU, THIS CHICKEN...

IT'S UNLIKE ANYTHING I'VE EVER TASTED. *DELICIOUS.*

IT'S VERY... UM... KATIE?

ARE YOU OKAY?

Max.

KATIE? YOU LOOK A LITTLE FLUSHED.

MAYBE YOU SHOULD SIT DOWN.

KATIE? ...I'M A DOCTOR...

HI.

KATIE! HEY!

HAVE YOU MET ADAM?

HI.

hand shake?

wait...

awkward

fist bump

LISTEN, I FEEL BAD ABOUT LAST TIME. WE DIDN'T REALLY GET TO TALK.

YEAH?

YEAH. MAYBE IF YOU HAVE A MINUTE TONIGHT--?

Things had all of a sudden gotten ugly.

WHAT THE HELL WAS WRONG WITH THAT BURGER?!

MOOAANN

← bathroom

NO NO NO NO NO NO

NGA AAA AA

whyyyy??

And after her 147th trip to the toilet, in a haze of nausea and delirium,

she found the little notebook in her hand and began to write.

104

REVISION #2

DOCTOR AND MRS. ANDRETTI. HI.

HOW'S THE CHICKEN? AMAZING?

THANK YOU.

WHAT?

WHA...?

HEY, MAX.

KATIE! HEY!

HAVE YOU MET ADAM?

YEAH, WE MET EARLIER.

WE DID?

HOW YA DOIN', MAX?

UHH...

CONFIDENT!

I'M... GOOD.

LISTEN, I FEEL BAD ABOUT LAST TIME.

UM, YEAH... WE DIDN'T REALLY GET TO TALK.

RIGHT. HERE'S THE THING: I'M A BUSY PERSON.

YOU DON'T EVEN HAVE A MINUTE FOR--

FOR WHAT, MAX?

His smile   faltered.

MAYBE IF YOU WANT TO TALK YOU SHOULD CALL INSTEAD OF, LIKE, STALKING ME, OKAY?

O-OKAY.

106

She left him there

to think about what he'd done.

And in the morning

she woke up

feeling amazing.

4

Rules

Arthur called as Katie was getting dressed.

HOW ARE THINGS?

THINGS ARE GREAT! AND WEIRD. ...THEY'RE WEIRD.

EXCELLENT. SO, YES, PERMITS HAVE BEEN DELAYED, THE CONTRACTOR IS BEING A PETULANT CHILD...

...BUT WHEN YOU GO IN THERE, PLEASE DON'T FREAK OUT ON HIM.

NOT YET, HA HA.

ARTHUR, I KNOW YOU JUST DID A FUNERAL AND YOU'RE PROBABLY MEGA BUMMED RIGHT NOW.

BUT THIS IS ALL GONNA WORK OUT. I HAVE A STRONG FEELING.

YEAH. YOU'RE RIGHT.

JUST SIGN IT RIGHT-- YEAH, THERE.

THANKS.

HELL YEAH!

AUTHORIZAT

SO HOW'S IT GOING? SEEMS LIKE WE WERE FURTHER ALONG LAST TIME. HA HA

HA HA. I KEEP TELLING MYSELF SHE'S JUST OLD, BUT EVERY STEP HAS BEEN... TRICKY. FOR EXAMPLE:

WE GO TO PUT YOUR BAR IN, BUT THE FLOOR ISN'T STRAIGHT. JOISTS BELOW US TURN OUT TO BE ROTTEN. BASEMENT'S CAVING IN. FOUNDATION'S CRUMBLING.

SHE'S A BEAST.

HACK OFF ONE HEAD, TWO MORE SHOW UP.

ARTHUR SAID THIS'S YOUR SECOND RESTAURANT. WHERE'S THE OTHER ONE AT?

FIRST AVE.

UP ON THE HILL? I BEEN THERE. NICE PLACE. GOOD BEER.

THANKS. WHY'S THERE A FIREPLACE HERE?

OH, WE FOUND IT BRICKED UP.

PROBABLY HASN'T SEEN LIGHT FOR SIXTY-ODD YEARS.

IT WAS LIKE A MUMMY'S TOMB IN THERE.

EW. GET RID OF IT. YOU'RE GETTING RID OF IT RIGHT?

HEY, IT'S YOUR BUILDING, LADY.

YOU WANT TO KEEP ANY OF THIS OLD JUNK?

111

And so Katie claimed a treasure from the ancient pile before they dumpstered the whole thing.

It didn't look sixty-odd years old. It looked a thousand years old.

Back at Seconds, she went downstairs to show off a little.

..A MUMMY'S TOMB?? WICKED!

WHAT IS THIS THING? A POT?

THE WORD I'D USE IS CAULDRON. PRETTY COOL, HUH?

WHAT'S A CAULDRON?

YO, DUMMY. IT'S LIKE AN OLD POT THAT BELONGS TO A WITCH.

...WHAT?

IGNORE THE BABIES, HAZEL. THEY'RE JUST JEALOUS.

JEALOUS OF YOUR BEAUTIFUL HAIR.

THERE'S DIRT IN THE BOTTOM OF YOUR WITCH'S POT.

...DIRT OR ASHES OR SOMETHING, SEE?

FWOOF

PAT
PAT
PAT

Some part of her brain thought the ashes might make good fertilizer.

After all,

she was going to need a lot of mushrooms.

She started with an even dozen.

116

117

Everyone's Drunk

GUYS... WHAT IF THE WORLD ENDS WHEN I TURN THIRTY?

UGH!

MOANNN

SHUT UP!

NOBODY CARES!

YOU AND ME ARE THE ONLY ONES LEFT, RAY.

WE *BUILT* THIS FRICKIN' RESTAURANT.

LEAVE ME OUT OF THIS.

...AND SHE ATE IT ANYWAY!

SHE ATE IT.

AUUGH

THAT'S LIKE THE WORST THING I EVER HEARD.

SHE ATE IT! LIKE... ALL OF IT!!!

POP

chew chew

REVISION #3

REVISION #4

HEY, ANDREW... WHAT TIME DO YOU GET OFF?

UHHH, IS THAT A TRICK QUESTION?

YOU INVENTED THIS JOB.

THEN I GUESS I SHOULD BE ASKING: WHAT TIME DO YOU *WANT* TO GET OFF?

S E X Y (?)

I LOVE YOU.

REVISION #5

All this having her cake and eating it too and also *not* having her cake and never eating it was...

...confusing?

NOT AT ALL! HEY DUDE.

SUP, K. WHERE YOU BEEN?

Katie had never liked cause and effect anyway.

IT'S A FLAWED SYSTEM!

Still, she had to admit that toying with the universe was a little unsettling.

SHE DID NOT.

KATIE ADMITTED NOTHING OF THE SORT.

Even so, her phone chimed with a certain inevitability.

1 new email
Doug (Contractor)

From: Dou
To: Arthur
CC: Katie
Re: Payme

Arthur--

As you kno
project in g

However, t

The bottom line
**I need $12,000 b
tomorrow.** It's
either that or we
walk.

Sorry. You know
have other jobs

Hey Arthur,

I'm seriously freaking out and I really need you to call me.

Hey Arthur,

I'm seriously fre ← ← ← ←

Hey Arthur,

I just got that email and I was wondering if you're dealing with it, or like, you know, um, if I can help, I guess? I don't mind handling stuff while you're gone! At all. Just let me know!

GRAB

TAP TAP TAP TAP TAP

Arthur?

Arthur

y dude

u there

Arthur

Hello?

SCROLL
SCROLL
SCROLL

Jen
Last called 11 months ago

Jenn
Last called 2 months ago

K

Katie (Me)

M

Max
Last called 3 months

N

Nick (D
Last called a

R

Ray

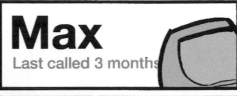

Max
Last called 3 months

twitch

Max
Last called 3 months ago

N

Nick (Dad)
Last called a week ago

HELLO?

...DAD?

KATIE? IS EVERY-THING OKAY?

UM... ACTUALLY... EVERYTHING'S...

...FINE.

ISN'T IT... UM... ALMOST YOUR BIRTHDAY?

JULY? ...I KNEW THAT.

I GUESS I JUST CALLED TO SAY I LOVE YOU?

123

124

125

PERSONAL SPACE, LIS.

SMELLS LIKE *MUSH-ROOMS.*

NO MORE.

TOO MANY--

WAIT A SEC!

LUCKNOW--

I COULD CHANGE IT ALL WITH A MUSHROOM! IT'S SO EASY!

WE WOULD HIRE A DIFFERENT CONTRACTOR, FOR STARTERS. THEN I'D GET IN THERE, TWEAK THINGS, *FIX* THINGS.

WHY DIDN'T I THINK OF THIS EARLIER?

NO.

WHY THE HELL NOT, LIS?

LIS'S MUSHROOMS.

LIS'S HOUSE.

VERY OLD.

THERE ARE RULES.

LIS, IT'S NOT THAT I DON'T RESPECT YOUR ADORABLE GOBLIN RULES...

...BUT I THINK I'VE BEEN DOING JUST FINE WITHOUT THEM.

ANYWAY, IT'S BEEN FUN CHATTING, BUT I'VE GOT A LOT OF WORK TO DO NOW.

THAT MEANS YOU SHOULD GO, BY THE WAY. IT'S A SOCIAL CUE.

NO.

WHAT NOW?

LIS'S MUSHROOMS. TAKING THEM AWAY.

OH REALLY? I'D LIKE TO SEE YOU *TRY*, LIS.

I HID THEM SOMEWHERE YOU'LL NEVER FIND THEM! I'M TIRED OF *HOUSE SPIRITS* MESSING WITH MY STUFF.

MY GOD, LIG, HAVE YOU EVER HEARD OF PANTS?

BLEAH

The mushroom, somehow, remained unchewed.

1. Write you
2. Ingest one m
3. Go to s
4. Wake

EVENTS MUST OCCUR O

EVENTS MUST OCCUR ON THESE PREMISES

Things had to have happened AT Seconds?

Lis hadn't followed her outside. Maybe Lis couldn't follow her outside.

If Lis was the house spirit of Seconds, and the mushrooms were some kind of extension of Lis, it almost made sense.

Katie wiped off the uneaten mushroom, threw it back in the witch's pot, and hid the whole thing in the back seat of her car.

At the very least she knew Lis wouldn't steal her stash.

133

134

OKAY, JUST DO YOUR THING.

1. Sweeping the hearth

KSH KSH

2. Feeding the fire

THEY LIKE TO SLEEP BY THE FIRE, SO I KEEP IT NICE!

3. Clothing drop

I GOT HER A NEW COAT.

ANIMAL PRINT. I DUNNO.

I HOPE SHE LIKES IT.

4. Bread on the rafters

ALWAYS FRESH BREAD, NEVER DAY-OLDS.

PATRICK SAVES ENDS FOR ME.

PLEASE DON'T TELL HIM WHAT I DO WITH THEM...

YOU FEED HER BREAD EVERY DAY? JUST BREAD? WOW.

YEAH... WHY WOW?

I MEAN... UH... WILL SHE GET FAT?

WAIT,.. BREAD MAKES YOU *FAT*?

SORRY...

NOW WHAT?

NOW WE WAIT AND SEE WHAT LIS DOES.

WE MAKE THINGS GOOD FOR HER, SHE MAKES THINGS GOOD FOR US, RIGHT?

RIGHT!

Y'KNOW, THIS WHOLE RITUAL MIGHT BE STUPID, BUT IT STILL MAKES SECONDS FEEL MORE LIKE HOME, EVEN IF--

EVEN IF NOBODY LIKES YOU?

S I P

THEY JUST DON'T KNOW YOU, DUDE.

HOW DO PEOPLE GET TO KNOW PEOPLE?

HELL IF I KNOW.

WHOA... SHHH

136

WHAT?

SHE'S UP THERE. SHE'S EATING THE BREAD.

SHE'S EATING THE BREAD LIKE A SQUIRREL.

OKAY... SHE'S DONE.

THAT WAS SO FAST!

I KNOW. OKAY, SHE'S ON THE MANTEL NOW...

SHE'S PICKING UP THE FUR COAT...

SHE'S...

CHOMP

SNRf

CHEW CHEW

SHOVE

blrkk

WHAT'S SO FUNNY? IS SHE WEARING IT? IS IT UGLY?

WHAT??

HA HA HA HA HA HA HA HA

138

OKAY, FACT: LIS IS *REAL*.

SHE'S A BEING, OR AN ENERGY, OR... OR SOMETHING. BUT SHE'S A REAL THING.

AND SHE ISN'T... HUMAN.

I DON'T THINK SO. SHE JUST APPEARS HUMAN TO US.

TO YOU.

TO ME.

... AND SHE REALLY LOOKS LIKE MY DRAWING?

SHE REALLY DOES. I DON'T GET IT AT ALL.

IT'S COOL... IT'S LIKE I *CREATED* SOMETHING.

BEFORE YOU STARTED TALKING TO ME, I FELT LIKE SHE WAS MY ONLY FRIEND.

AND SHE WASN'T EVEN REAL.

NOW SHE'S REAL, AND YOU'RE REAL, AND...

140

HE WAS HERE THE OTHER NIGHT...

MAX. HE USED TO WORK HERE.

IS HE YOUR EX?

I GUESS. WE DATED FOR... FOUR YEARS, ALMOST.

FOUR YEARS? WHAT HAPPENED?

IT'S... COMPLICATED.

BUT WHY'D HE COME IN? 'CAUSE HE MISSED YOU?

I DON'T EVEN KNOW WHAT HE EVER SAW IN ME.

HE WAS A FRIEND OF RAY'S, AND I JUST NEEDED GENERAL KITCHEN HELP, SO HE WAS IT.

(Max, five minutes before his first shift)

I HATED HIM AT FIRST. HE WAS LIKE ANDREW TIMES A BILLION. SUCH HOT SHIT. LEATHER JACKET, BLONDE ON HIS ARM. AND HE COULD BARELY COOK.

SELFIE!

BUT WE COULD *TALK*. WE WORKED TOGETHER EVERY NIGHT AND THE CONVERSATION NEVER ENDED.

SO YEAH, ME AND MAX HOOKING UP WAS INEVITABLE.

HE GOT BETTER IN THE KITCHEN. WE MADE EACH OTHER STRONGER.

WHEN SECONDS GOT POPULAR WE HAD TO HIRE NEW LINE COOKS AND START SPLITTING THE WEEK.

Andrew (TRAINEE)

WE NEVER SAW EACH OTHER ANYMORE. THAT GOT HARD.

AND I GUESS WHAT WE HAD WASN'T THAT STRONG.

BUT... WHAT HAPPENED?

UGH... I DON'T KNOW.

EMPTY

HE WANTED ME TO MOVE IN WITH HIM, BUT I WAS SAVING SO MUCH MONEY BY LIVING UPSTAIRS...

WE STARTED RESENTING EACH OTHER ABOUT WORK, AND, AND...

I GUESS IT IS COMPLICATED.

NO, IT ISN'T. IT'S... I DIDN'T TELL HIM.

I DIDN'T TELL HIM ABOUT MY NEW RESTAURANT. I THOUGHT IT'D FALL APART. I COULDN'T CONVINCE MYSELF IT WAS REAL. THEN HE FOUND OUT FROM SOMEONE ELSE, AND THAT WAS IT. HE WALKED.

Snf (drunk)

HAZEL...

LIS GAVE ME MUSHROOMS.

143

WHAT?

SHE GAVE ME SPECIAL MUSHROOMS AND I'VE BEEN EATING THEM.

THEY CHANGE THINGS, HAZEL.

BUT NOT EVERYTHING. JUST WHAT HAPPENS HERE.

ADULT LIFE IS TERRIBLE, HAZEL. NEVER GROW UP.

EVERYTHING'S COMPLICATED, AND THERE ARE TOO MANY RULES, AND YOU CAN ONLY CHANGE THINGS THAT--

WAIT! WHOA.

I COULD USE A MUSHROOM TO TELL MAX!

OUR WHOLE RELATIONSHIP HAPPENED RIGHT HERE.

I COULD FIX IT.

...

144

The next thing she knew, she was writing.

Writing about Max.

REVISION #6

ALL GOOD, KAY?

HEY.

I LITERALLY JUST HAD THIS IDEA.

OH?

I... WOULD LIKE TO OPEN A SECOND RESTAURANT.

IS THIS YOUR WAY OF ASKING ME TO BE A PART OF IT?

And even here, in this perfect weird fugue state...

...Y-YEAH!

...she had to suppress a surge of panic.

YEAH, OF COURSE!

146

What
was
this?

What
was
she
seeing
now?

She
didn't
like
it at
all.

And
when
she
woke
up,

there
he
was.

5
Max

KATIE

WHAT'S

YOUR

PROBLEM

She
woke
him
up
the
rest
of
the
way.

Afterward,
he took a long
shower in her
tub.

(Which
was
weird.)

Meanwhile, Katie took stock of her new and improved life.

WHAT THE HELL...?

Her home had become strange and boy-centric.

Max *lived* here.

Max *lived* here?

WE LIVE... ...TOGETHER?

Lis wasn't happy.

But Katie didn't even notice.

Katie was busy flipping out.

A boy lived in her house, and his shit was everywhere.

The giant TV. The mess. *Video games??*

IT'S LIKE I DON'T EVEN KNOW HIM!

ZBOZ420

BIG BABY BEACH VOLLEYBALL

ZBOZ420

MIAMI JETSKI 420

When had Max ever once in his life played a guitar?

DO ALL BOYS PLAY GUITAR?

TWANG

Where was her favorite chair? Why'd they have his gross old couch?

Half the wardrobe was suddenly his clothes.

T-shirts and work shirts and jeans and blazers and all of it enormous.

WAIT... WHERE'S THE REST OF MY STUFF?

She buried her face in it.

I LOVE THE SMELL! I *LOVE* IT!!

(Or maybe she was taking deep breaths to avoid hyperventilating.)

NO.

153

She dressed cute.

She felt newly confident.

She felt cool.

She pushed away her questions and confusion.

This was good. It was just good.

HI.

HI...

KATIE. REALLY?

MMM. MMMAX. MAX MAX MAX MAX MAX.

WE HAVE WORK, KATIE.

BUT *MAAAX!!!*

154

Max went straight for the driver's side.

Her car keys were already in his pocket.

No-one but her had ever driven that car before.

This was love, right?

Love couldn't be a bad thing.

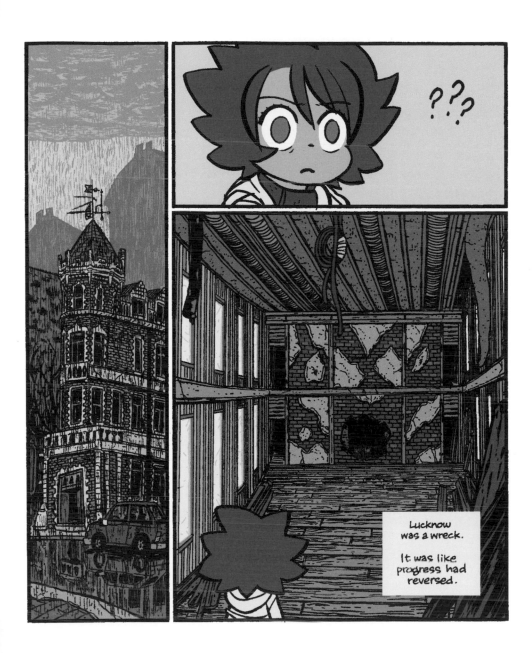

???

Lucknow was a wreck.

It was like progress had reversed.

Something was crushing her. Some unseen force. She could barely stand. This was insanity.

It had gotten worse.

She slowly realized Max was talking to the guy without her.

YOU GOTTA GIVE US A FEW DAYS, DOUG.

OUR PARTNER IS OUT OF TOWN. YOU KNOW THAT.

$18,000, BUDDY. OR I'M GONE.

EIGHTEEN?! IT WAS *TWELVE* YESTERDAY!

IT WAS ALWAYS EIGHTEEN, LADY, BUT THAT'S A MOOT POINT BECAUSE I DON'T SEE YOU PAYING ME SO I GUESS I'LL SEE YOU IN *HELL*.

YOU...

YOU PIECE OF HUMAN GARBAGE

I WILL **FUCK** YOU UP

KATIE. SETTLE.

KEEP HER IN CHECK, MAX.

WATCH ME PULL UP THE EMAIL YOU SENT LAST NIGHT, *DOUG!!*

CALL ME A LIAR...

bottom line ed $18,000 rrow. It's r that or w

She remembered it. She *remembered* it.

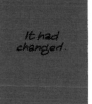

...

It had changed.

159

What else had changed?

What was happening to her?

IF YOU GET THE FUNDS, GIVE ME A CALL.

YOU AND YOUR WIFE HAVE A NICE DAY.

WIFE?! EXCUSE ME, YOU SEXIST DICK--

WE'RE MARRIED NOW?!

So Katie didn't have a restaurant. She had a shell. She had a husk.

At least she had Max now.

Her god damn husband.

He'd managed to get Arthur on the phone.

He was keeping his voice down.

Excluding her.

Taking care of things.

Just like she'd wanted.

FOR LEASE
771 TALMADGE
JUST REDUCED

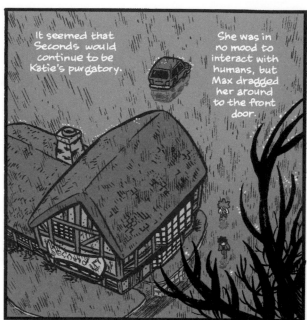

It seemed that Seconds would continue to be Katie's purgatory.

She was in no mood to interact with humans, but Max dragged her around to the front door.

OH, UH... WELCOME TO SECONDS, BUT WE'RE ACTUALLY NOT OPEN YET--

MAX!!

HEY, GUYS!

MAAAAX! WE NEVER SEE YOU ANYMORE!

WE MISS YOU, MAX!

They loved him.

Why did they love him?

Why did they love him and not her?

She didn't know this photo.

She had no memory of this day.

She hadn't lived it.

HEY. EVERYTHING OKAY?

EVERYTHING? NO.

IS HE AROUND?

WHO, MAX? HE WENT UPSTAIRS TO MAKE SOME CALLS.

COOL.

SMOOCH

CLUTCH

WHAT ARE YOU DOING?!

164

WHAT DO YOU MEAN WHAT AM I DOING?

I... I'M *MARRIED*, ANDREW.

WE CAN'T KEEP DOING THIS!

COME ON, KATIE. THAT NIGHT WE SHARED-- YOU FELT IT TOO.

What night? She'd erased that night.

I *ERASED* THAT NI-- I MEAN *THAT NIGHT NEVER HAPPENED!*

YOU CAN PRETEND ALL YOU WANT, KATIE.

YOUR HEART KNOWS WHAT'S UP.

THAT'S... SO CHEESY...

Had some other version of the night she'd spent with Andrew taken place in her new married life?

Or... had this changed in some other way?

SHHH. I'M JUST GONNA GO WITH IT.

AHEM.

SUPER CASUAL

SO, YOU REDUCE THE WINE AND BROTH FOR...

KATIE. COME IN FOR A SEC.

165

WHAT'S UP, RAYMOND? WE WERE JUST, UM--

OH *STOP.* I KNOW ABOUT YOU AND ANDREW.

. . .

I MEAN *WHAT* ABOUT US? BECAUSE WE WERE REALLY ONLY--

KATIE. EVERYONE KNOWS. EVERYONE BUT MAX, I MEAN.

AND THE ONLY REASON HE *DOESN'T* KNOW IS BECAUSE HE'S BEEN SO BUSY WITH HIS NEW RESTAURANT.

UH, IT'S ACTUALLY *MY* NEW RESTAURANT.

BUT YOU SEE WHAT I'M SAYING, KATIE.

I DON'T KNOW THAT I DO, RAY.

I'M SAYING STOP. YOU AND ANDREW. WHATEVER IT IS. JUST STOP.

PLEASE. IT'S DISRESPECTFUL. TO MAX. TO EVERYONE.

OH. OH, THAT.

166

HAZEL!

LET'S TALK! CAN WE TALK? I NEED TO TALK.

GAK. HI...

WHAT'S UP? WHAT ARE YOU UP TO? HOW ARE YOU?

UM... I'M A BIT EARLY FOR MY SHIFT, SO I WAS GONNA GO OUT AND DO SOME SHOPPING...

COOL! SOUNDS GOOD!

. . . .

SHE'S WEARING HEELS EVEN THOUGH SHE'S ALREADY TALL

HOW IS THAT FAIR?

169

I WANT TO SEE THE MAGIC MUSHROOM PATCH! IS IT LIKE A FAIRY RING?

UMM...

I THINK IT'S SAFEST IF I DON'T-- LIKE, YOU KNOW--

IF THEY FELL INTO THE, UM, WRONG HANDS--

OH GOSH! YOU'RE RIGHT!

I KNOW. I'M SO SORRY.

LYING

I GUESS THERE'S ONE QUESTION ON MY MIND.

IF WE ASSUME SHE USES THE MUSHROOMS TO CHANGE LITTLE THINGS FOR US EVERY DAY...

...WHY WOULD SHE START LETTING *YOU* CHANGE *BIG* THINGS?

Katie suddenly remembered the first thing. The accident.

But it didn't seem appropriate to tell Hazel about that.

HOW WAS YOUR DAY?

UM, CONFUSING AND TERRIBLE. HOW WAS YOURS?

...SO YOU THINK SPIKE'S THIS TOTAL BAD GUY, BUT IN SEASON SEVEN, HE SHOWS HIS TRUE--

...ARE YOU LISTENING?

Back in the basement, Katie noticed that the office door was ajar...

SIGH

Max
(29 years old)
Status: bummed

GRAB

spl ish

clink!

SIP

173

THIS IS THE ROOM WHERE WE MET.

YOU WERE SO COOL.

I WAS ONLY PLAYING IT COOL 'CAUSE YOU WERE SO COOL.

PSSH.

NO, REALLY.

YOU HAD YOUR OWN KITCHEN. I WAS BUMMING AROUND. WASTING MY TIME.

I RESPECTED THE HELL OUT OF YOU BEFORE I EVER WALKED IN HERE, KATIE.

IT'S TAKEN ME THIS LONG TO EVEN BEGIN TO CATCH UP.

He'd never opened up like this before.

It was like she'd tricked her way into a deeper relationship without having to do any of the heavy lifting. Pretty awesome!

THIS IS ALSO THE ROOM WHERE WE DECIDED ON LUCKNOW.

LAST FALL. REMEMBER? US AND ARTHUR.

LOOKING THROUGH THOSE REAL ESTATE PORTFOLIOS. MAKING THE WRONG CHOICE.

174

OH, DUDE, NO. NO NO. IT IS WHAT IT IS.

WHAT'S DONE IS DONE. WE... WE MOVE FORWARD, RIGHT?

ARTHURISMS.

HE'S OUT OF TOWN. SOMEONE'S GOTTA SAY 'EM.

NAH. FACE IT, KAY, LUCKNOW'S A MONEY PIT.

WE BLEW IT.

IF WE'D PICKED TALMADGE, I BET WE'D BE IN THERE RIGHT NOW, COOKING UP A STORM.

Lucknow had been Katie's choice.

In her version of that day, it'd been just her and Arthur in the room. She'd insisted on Lucknow.

She'd probably argued just as hard with Max in this version.

But why? What did it all add up to? Nothing. Her past self was clearly a pretentious idiot.

Was Max right?

Had she blown it?

182

183

It was a tree.

At the junctures of its branches, she saw points of light.

Seconds was nestled in the branches, tiny and perfect.

Then it was gone.

She spotted it again, somewhere else this time.

Lis was trying to show her something.

This meant something.

SHFFF

185

Whatever that was, it was kind of amazing.

Katie was kind of awed and kind of astonished.

On the other hand, she had no idea what any of that awesome and astonishing shit was supposed to mean.

She was tired, and confused, and tired of being confused, and so...

CHOMP

CHEW CHEW CHEW

187

GULP

She hid under the covers. But in like a defiant and cool way.

SHUT UP.

REVISION #7

YOU OKAY, BABY?

192

HMM... WELL, IF THERE'S A SCARY MONSTER DOWN IN THE KITCHEN, I'M NOT SURPRISED IT'D BE YOU, BABY.

THANKS...

HOWEVER, IF WE ANALYZE YOUR DREAM FROM A PSYCHOLOGICAL STANDPOINT, IT'S CLEARLY ALL ABOUT--

SHUT UP!

WHOMP

MMF MRPH MAH MF

She loved him. Or something.

I DO. I REALLY DO.

She felt safe in his arms. She needed him now.

The restaurant, the house spirit-- right now none of it was as important to her as Max.

Her god damn *husband*.

YOU DO WHAT?

SHH.

194

195

Now Max was like *upset* or something. "Their" new restaurant?

How was Katie supposed to know which semantics were off limits in a relationship that was a mystery to her?

It was *her* restaurant. It wasn't for sharing.

SO... THINGS ARE GOING WELL AT TALMADGE?

I GUESS *"WE"* MADE THE RIGHT CHOICE?

Nothing. He gave her the silent treatment the whole way.

Which didn't bother her. She could fix him later if needed.

Under budget.
Under schedule.

Talmadge was
almost finished.

The bastards
had been right.

She gawked at the perfect wall sconces.

the ideal tiles,

the bar she'd dreamed about,

all the precious shit she'd wanted.

But...

... the layout was wrong.

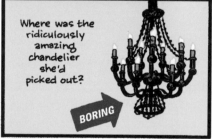
Where was the ridiculously amazing chandelier she'd picked out?

BORING

And why was this color going on the walls right now?

HIDEOUS

She'd given up Lucknow. She'd gotten this instead. All for a guy.

SHUDDER TO THINK

HIM

Was he worth it?

WHAT? YES!

OF... OF COURSE HE WAS.

Graphic Designer(?)

They all said "MK II"...

What the hell was this?

THEY ALL SAY MK II...

There had to be some kind of mistake.

I SURE HOPE SO!

HEY... WHAT HAPPENED TO CALLING IT "KATIE'S"?

I LIKE THE LOGO WE PICKED.

Last fall. Last fall was too far. The farther back she went, the more wide-ranging the ramifications of her changes.

AND MKII IS A GOOD NAME. I THINK IT'S STRONG.

She tried to imagine another Katie, a Katie who thought "MKII" was a good name for a restaurant. Where was she now? When had she given up on life?

MAX AND KATIE'S SECOND RESTAURANT. IT'S CLEVER.

I KNOW IT ISN'T EXACTLY WHAT YOU WANTED.

What was the precise moment at which the two Katies had diverged?

BUT YOU NEED TO COMPROMISE ONCE IN A WHILE, Y'KNOW?

UM, WHERE ARE WE GOING?

They were going to Lucknow. She had to see what was happening at Lucknow.

It was a ruin.

It'd always been there, as far back as she could remember. Old, junky, run-down. But never like this.

This seemed beyond repair. Unsalvageable.

LOOK AT THIS DUMP. WE MADE THE RIGHT CHOICE.

Y-YEAH...

Had she caused this?

Where was she?

UMM... I'LL BE RIGHT IN.

SURE.

She'd decided to bring the mushrooms inside.

Their presence in her car was starting to freak her out.

She didn't realize, however,

that one mushroom remained, lost in the back seat.

Katie stashed the witch's pot in the back of her nightstand.

She couldn't see Lis anywhere.

But Lis was there.

And after, when she went back downstairs,

Katie got turned around between the stairs and the kitchen, which was weird--

--it's not like the hallway was a maze.

HEY, WHERE'S HAZEL?

KEEPING TABS ON YOUR NEW GIRLFRIEND IS NOT OUR JOB.

OH *SNAP!* I CAN'T BELIEVE YOU ACTUALLY SAID IT!

DON'T SAY "OH SNAP," DUDE.

ANDREW.

THIS HAS TO END.

PFFT.

YOU'RE SUCH A HYPOCRITE, KATIE.

I'M WHAT?

YOU'RE USING ME.

I'M *WHAT?*

YOU'RE MY BOSS AND YOU'RE OLDER AND YOU'RE MARRIED AND--

OLDER?! WHAT DOES THAT HAVE TO DO WITH ANYTHING?

OH COME ON. I'M NOT AN IDIOT.

YOU *ARE* AN IDIOT. WE WERE JUST HAVING FUN. BOTH OF US.

AND IT *STOPPED* BEING FUN, DUDE.

OKAY. YEAH! I *AM* AN IDIOT.

'CAUSE I *RESPECT* YOU. I WANTED TO WORK HERE BECAUSE OF YOU. YOUR FOOD.

BUT I'M NOTHING TO YOU.

WHAT?

LIKE THAT FUCKING-- THAT GIRL HAZEL? WHY HER?

WHY CAN'T YOU TALK TO ME LIKE THAT? I WANTED US TO BE FRIENDS.

DUDE. ANDREW... I DIDN'T KNOW YOU FELT LIKE--

I GOTTA GO.

WHAT? HANG ON A SEC!

I DON'T LIKE IT BACK HERE ANYMORE. THE WALK-IN... YOU DON'T FEEL THAT?

FEEL WHAT?

I DON'T KNOW. NEVER MIND.

But she did feel it.

The shadow. She knew it was real.

I DON'T FEEL ANYTHING.

Um, yeah, she did, actually.

208

When she got upstairs, Max was getting his jacket on to leave.

WHERE ARE YOU GOING?

OUT.

HEY, ARE YOU STILL PISSED ABOUT THE WHOLE "NAMING THE RESTAURANT AFTER ME" THING?

BECAUSE IT WAS A JOKE, OKAY?

IT IS?

OH... OKAY...

NAH.

IT'S FINE.

SCARY FAKE SMILE

WELL...

BYE...

There seemed to be a distinct possibility that it was not fine.

As she watched, the nightstand moved on its own, waddling toward the end of the bed.

THIS IS SO DUMB.

HOP

LIS'S MUSHROOMS.

SNFF

CREEAKK

LIIIIIISSSSS... WAAAIIIIIT...

RECOIL

VANISH!

...What?

What was it?
What caused
Lis to react
so violently?

Was it the
witch's pot?

...WHY?

There were six mushrooms in the pot.

How many changes had she made now?

She tried to do the math, but immediately gave up.

toss

REVISION #8

REVISION #9

 And like that, the day was over, and she could barely remember what she needed to change for tomorrow.

They had started cooking, hammering out the details of their new menu. Every moment should have been a delight, but somehow none of them were.

Max was always disappointed in her, as if she'd been perfect once. As if he was now.

Four left.

She could get it right with four more. No problem.

REVISION #10

PANT
PANT
PANT
PANT

SHH.
IT'S
OKAY.

And
Max was
there.

And she
just started
sobbing.

221

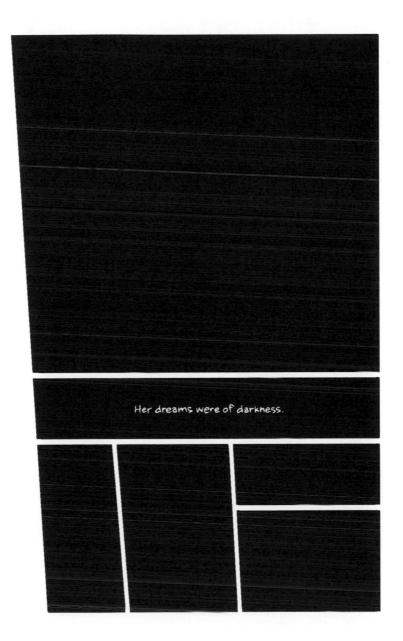

Katie
fell
asleep
again.

Her dreams were of darkness.

She woke up,

and there was a glow.

6
Control

When Katie woke up, she was back in her normal bedroom with Max asleep beside her.

She decided to take an early-morning drive. Away from here.

She
ended
up at
Hazel's
house.

She wondered:
was there a house
spirit here too?

It seemed rude to barge
in, so she texted.

Are you home?

BZZ

?

Like are you
at home

BZZ

yes

Ok I'm coming in

BZZ

what

HEY...

GOOD MORNING...

LOOK AT THIS ROOM! YOU'RE LIKE A PRINCESS, HAZEL.

YEAH, IT'S MORTIFYING.

STARE

DID YOU... CUT YOUR HAIR?

UM... NO.

SHF
SHFF

SO I GUESS YOU'VE BEEN... UH... PRETTY BUSY?

YEAH. THINGS HAVE BEEN KINDA... BAD-ISH?

MAN, YOU HAVE A *LOT* OF CLOTHES.

She wanted to tell Hazel everything. But she couldn't keep track of what she'd already said, of what had or hadn't happened, of what she even knew anymore.

THE OTHER NIGHT, WHAT DID YOU WANT TO TALK ABOUT?

OH... UM...

NOTHING.

A few days of friendship neglect and things were this awkward already.

HOW DO YOU AFFORD ALL THIS STUFF?

I THRIFT. ALSO, I DON'T HAVE A LIFE.

FWUMP

NO BOYFRIEND?

NO...

I HAVEN'T ACTUALLY... DATED.

EVER?

NUH-UH

NOT INTO BOYS?

I... DON'T KNOW YET. UNDECIDED.

OH... WELL, THAT'S COOL!

LOOK AT ALL THESE SHOES...

OH! I FOUND THIS OLD PICTURE BOOK IN THE ATTIC--

I DON'T KNOW IF IT'S FROM WHEN I WAS A KID, OR WHEN MY MOM WAS, OR--

MY AUNT USED TO READ IT TO ME. I CAN'T BELIEVE I FORGOT ALL ABOUT IT!

GOOD HOUSE, BAD HOUSE.

I THINK I CHEWED OFF THAT CORNER...

GOOD HOUSE, BAD HOUSE

THIS IS CREEPY FEEL'N... IT LOOKS *JUST* LIKE SECONDS!

NO IT DOESN'T. SETTLE DOWN.

OKAY, SO THERE'S THIS FAMILY AND THEY JUST MOVED TO A NEW HOUSE.

BUT ONLY THE LITTLEST DAUGHTER REALIZES THEY ACCIDENTALLY BROUGHT THEIR OLD HOUSE SPIRIT ALONG.

I GUESS HE WAS SLEEPING IN THIS OLD TRUNK.

OF COURSE, THERE'S A HOUSE SPIRIT IN THEIR NEW HOUSE TOO.

SO THE TWO HOUSE SPIRITS FIGHT OVER THE HOUSE.

IT'S, LIKE, FUNNY? BUT... KINDA DARK.

THE FAMILY CAN'T KEEP BOTH SPIRITS HAPPY, 'CAUSE DIFFERENT THINGS MAKE THEM HAPPY.

EVERY HOUSE SPIRIT WANTS TO LIVE IN A DIFFERENT KIND OF HOUSE, I GUESS.

ANYWAY, THE FAMILY TRIES EVERYTHING, BUT IN THE END THIS HOUSE "GOES BAD."

AND THEN WHAT HAPPENS??

UM...

...THEY MOVE AWAY.

WHAT?!

LISTEN, KATIE...

THE LAST FEW WEEKS HAVE BEEN... *WEIRD* AT SECONDS.

HAVEN'T YOU FELT IT?

Yes. Definitely.

NOPE.

236

I'VE BEEN WORKING EXTRA HARD TO KEEP LIS HAPPY, BUT IT ISN'T HELPING.

AND I THINK...

I THINK *THIS* IS WHAT'S HAPPENING.

GOOD HOUSE, BAD HOUSE

WHAT?

YOU MEAN THAT BOOK FOR LITTLE BABIES?

THE TWO HOUSE SPIRITS THING?

. . .

LIKE... AT SECONDS? IN REAL LIFE?

...HOW?

I THINK YOU INVITED SOMETHING IN.

The
door.
The
shadow.

She knew
it was
real. She'd
known all
along.

She'd invited it
into her home.
It didn't matter
how or why.

What mattered
was that she
had to face it.
And she was
ready.

She was
almost
ready.

She was
getting
there.

She walked
with purpose.
For like a
second.

The kitchen
seemed
farther than
ever. The
halls kept
stretching.

The basement
was changing,
evolving, with
every revision.
Katie hadn't
caused this--

--it
had.

And then

things went

HEY,
CHEF.

way
past
weird.

241

They were
skeletons.

Skeletons were working
in her kitchen.

DISHWASHER

HEY,
BOSS.

PREP COOK

HEY,
BOSS.

FOOD RUNNER

...

PATRICK

HEY,
BOSS.

!!!!!

242

WELL, I THOUGHT ABOUT IT A LOT, AND...

KATIE, COULD YOU MAYBE LOOK AT ME FOR LIKE FIVE SECONDS?

B-BUT HE'S--

Smiling?

...or just a skull?

HE'S *WHAT?* A SKELETON? GET OVER YOURSELF, DUDE.

LISTEN... I REALIZED YOU'RE RIGHT.

I AM?

WE'RE NEVER GONNA BE FRIENDS, KATIE.

AND WHATEVER PHYSICAL ATTRACTION THERE WAS BETWEEN US IS OVER.

WHAT? I DIDN'T SAY THAT.

I DIDN'T SAY EITHER OF THOSE.

I STILL THINK--

NO. LISTEN. I PUT IN MY NOTICE WITH RAY.

YOU WHAT?

I'M MOVING ON.

SO ONE WAY OR ANOTHER, THIS, *US*--

--IT'S OVER, KATIE.

And Max was there.

And Max had heard everything.

Things were bad.

Things couldn't really be worse.

But she could still fix it.

She just needed to use a mushroom right away.

Three left.

Three was enough.

But then she couldn't find the little notebook.

HEY... ARE YOU LOOKING FOR SOMETHING IN THERE?

BECAUSE I FOUND SOMETHING. AND I THINK IT BELONGS TO YOU.

He had it.

MY MISTAKES

Max had her mistakes in his hot little hand.

So... things were worse.

248

WHAT IS THIS, KATIE?

WHAT THE HELL IS IT?

Oh no.

OH NO.

I THOUGHT IT WAS LIKE A DIARY AT FIRST.

SOME KIND OF WEIRD, GUILTY DIARY.

Oh no no no.

NO

She had to get it back.

BUT... YOU READ ON AND IT'S FULL OF MADE-UP GARBAGE.

COND CHANCE AWAIT

1. Write your mistake
2. Ingest one mushroom
3. Go to sleep
4. Wake anew

UNREALITY.

VERY DETAILED UNREALITY.

ALSO, YOUR SPELLING IS ATROCIOUS...

The rules were unspecific. Write your mistake?

They didn't even mention the notebook.

rite your mistake
gest one mushroom
3. Go to sleep
4. Wake anew

No
time
for
sleep.
No
time
for
rules.

CHOMP

KATIE!

BAM
BAM

BAM
BAM

KA--

REVISION #11

She
felt it.

The
world
shuddered
and
changed.

She
felt
it.

She
half fell
into the
dresser.

The
pounding
on the
door had
stopped.

Max
was
gone.

Katie changed her sweater,

just so she could take the last two mushrooms.

and keep them with her.

1   2

She couldn't let them out of her sight. The stakes were too high now.

Then she headed

???????

The state of the dining room did not dispel this notion.

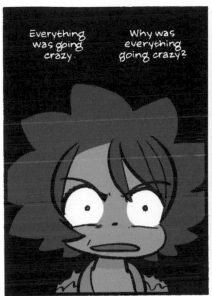

Everything was going crazy.

Why was everything going crazy?

Why would there be a band at her restaurant?

Were they really skeletons, or was she seeing things?

...HOW IS A SKELETON PLAYING A WOODWIND?

HEY, BOSS!

WHAT THE HELL ARE YOU WEARING?

WHAT THE HELL ARE THEY ALL WEARING?

UM... WHAT'S GOING ON?

WELL, THIS IS A *RESTAURANT*, AND THESE PEOPLE ARE HERE FOR A "MEAL"...

I MEAN WHY ARE THE SERVERS DRESSED LIKE... *THAT?*

WHAT, NOW YOU DON'T LIKE THE UNIFORMS? YOU HELPED PICK THEM, KATIE.

I GUESS I HELPED HIRE ALL THOSE SKELETONS IN THE KITCHEN TOO?

HELPED? NO. THE SKELETONS WERE 100% YOU, CHEF.

YOU CAN SEE THEM TOO?!

YOU'RE STARTING TO WORRY ME, KATIE.

259

The
kitchen
was hot
and
dark and
impossibly
far
from the
stairs.

And
Max
was
back.

And he
smiled,
because he
loved her
again.

Because
he didn't
remember
what had
happened.

Because
what had
happened
hadn't
happened.

She loved him, and he loved her, and that was all that mattered now.

The other stuff was--

She'd only
blinked.

I
LOVE
YOU,
MAXY
BABY.

I
LOVE
YOU
TOO,
YANA
BABY.

I
LOVE
YOU
TOO.

MAX.

No.

THE LAST MUSHROOM

SLIP

... OH, HEY. WHERE *IS* EVERYONE? I'M SLAMMED HERE!! I NEED FOUR RIBEYES FROM THE WALK-IN, OKAY?

MAX...?

Even moments later, Hazel couldn't say with certainty that she'd seen Lis, or anything at all.

Either way, it was time to get the hell out of Seconds. Maybe never to return.

 Hazel sat still and silent the whole way,

 clinging to the old storybook like a lifeline.

 Snow fell thick and fast. Everything outside her car was blank, white,

 as if the world

was being erased.

And still, Lucknow was a ruin.

Why?

Of everything that had happened, why this?

THAT WAS SUPPOSED TO BE MY NEW RESTAURANT.

LOOK AT IT NOW.

WHAT AM I SUPPOSED TO BE S-SEEING?

I USED TO STARE AT IT EVERY DAY. THERE WAS SOMETHING *ABOUT* IT.

NOW THERE JUST... ISN'T.

7
Can't Go Back

The witch's pot.

If she could find it, if she could bring it back--

IT'D FIX EVERYTHING!

...well... Maybe it'd help, anyway.

First of all, she had to get Hazel home safely.

I MUST HAVE TAKEN A WRONG-- HMM.

UM, HAZEL...? WHERE DO YOU LIVE?

I DON'T... KNOW.

blink

GOOD HOUSE, BAD HOUSE

And like that, she was at the start again,

a little bit closer to the end.

281

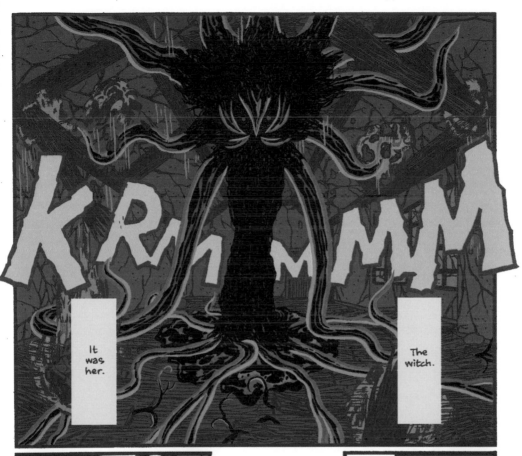

KRMMM

It was her.

The witch.

VANISH!

DAMN IT, LIS!

She
woke
up,

relieved,
so relieved,

and then she
remembered

FLOP

she was alone.

WHUMP

This wasn't Max. This was an inanimate object.

And this place...

THIS WORLD IS QUIET NOW.

The voice came from above.

THIS WORLD...?

THIS KATIE LEFT.

LEFT IT TO ROT.

EACH KATIE LEAVES.

THEY ALL LEAVE.

EVERY REVISION...

...WAS A **WORLD**.

And for one second, Katie understood: each point of light, each junction,

was not just a new time,

but a new place.

Another Seconds. Another Katie.

Every time she woke up it was as a different person.

293

294

ALL OUR CHOICES BROUGHT US HERE.

WE PUSHED PEOPLE AWAY. I ERASED ANDREW! YOU **KILLED** LIS!

NOW LOOK AT US. ALONE TOGETHER!

I KNOW YOU'VE HAD IT WORSE. YOU'VE BEEN ALONE FOR A LONG TIME.

A MAGIC MUSHROOM ISN'T GOING TO FIX THAT.

BUT YOU AREN'T ALONE. **I'M HERE NOW.** I'M IN THIS WORLD WITH YOU!

I KNOW IT ISN'T THE GREATEST, BUT WE CAN STILL AT LEAST *TRY* TO MAKE IT A LITTLE BETTER!

DON'T YOU WANT TO TRY?

297

She returned the pot to its filthy, forgotten fireplace.

She didn't have matches.

She didn't have anything.

But the fire started itself.

WHOOOOOOOSH

A piece of Lis's dresser remained. And there she was, curled up inside it like a tiny cat.

Katie was hardly shaking anymore.

She gave Lis's last mushroom back.

The cold didn't matter now.

She curled up beside her house spirit

and went to sleep.

She
woke
up.

308

OH, HEY. WELCOME BACK.

SPOILER WARNING: YOU'RE IN THE HOSPITAL.

WHAT? WHY?

WHY ARE *YOU* HERE? ARE YOU BACK, OR DID YOU EVER LEAVE, OR...?

UH... IN RESPONSE TO YOUR FIRST QUESTION:

YOU PASSED OUT. EXHAUSTION. MALNOURISHMENT, HYPOTHERMIA. THEY SAID ALL THAT WAS IN YOUR STOMACH WAS... MUSHROOMS?

...

AND LET ME JUST SAY I'M GENUINELY OFFENDED THAT A CHEF OF YOUR CALIBER WOULD EVER FORGET TO EAT.

SCARED THE SHIT OUT OF ME.

BUT WHERE DID YOU COME FROM? WHAT WORLD IS THIS?

WHAT CHANGED?

WHO'S... WHAT? WHERE'S WHEN?

Arthur just kinda smiled at her and rolled his eyes.

309

310

BUT THAT MEANS WE'RE BACK AT THE START.

NOTHING CHANGED.

But

something HAD changed.

WAIT.

WHY ARE YOU HERE?

WE'RE FRIENDS.

YEAH, BUT HOW ARE WE FRIENDS?

WE DIDN'T BECOME FRIENDS UNTIL--

--UNTIL YOU TALKED TO ME?

And Hazel told her side of the story:

How one day her weird interests unexpectedly became the focus of conversation with a person who had previously seemed intimidating.

An accidental friendship.

Somehow, through all the changes, this one thing had remained.

Maybe she was still feeling weak, but this was a lot for Katie to take. She got a little sobby.

I NEED TO BECOME A BETTER PERSON, ETC.

SHH, IT'S OKAY.

HAZEL... THANKS.

ANY TIME.

UM... YOUR HAND IS KIND OF... SLIMY.

SHIT, SORRY. OINTMENTS AND STUFF.

IT ACTUALLY KINDA HURTS TO TOUCH YOU...

Where was she now?

How many empty worlds had she left behind?

When Arthur drove her home, she wasn't sure what would be waiting for her.

But it was him.

And Katie's life was perfect for just one moment.

HEY...

HEY.

KATIE, I--

YEAH?

UH... I DON'T KNOW. I GOT NOTHING TO SAY.

I WAS KINDA HOPING YOU'D CUT ME OFF AND SAY SOMETHING DEEP...

I WOULD HAVE HAD A WITTY RESPONSE, AND--

OH, SO IT'S *MY* FAULT?!

COME ON. I WAS JOKING. IT'S NOT YOUR FAULT.

GOOD. BECAUSE I *DON'T* APOLOGIZE.

314

315

ME? I'M TIRED, MAN.

TIRED OF FAKING MY FAKE-ASS WAY THROUGH LIFE WITHOUT YOU, I GUESS.

YOU'RE TIRED?

...

WELL... I'M MORE TIRED THAN YOU.

WAY MORE.

WH U M P

NOW GET IN THE KITCHEN AND MAKE ME A SANDWICH.

WOW.

That spring, they repainted Seconds for the first time since it opened.

AND IT LOOKS BETTER THAN EVER!

THANK YOU.

Life at the restaurant returned to normal.

BORING OLD NORMAL OLD SECONDS!

Hazel cut her hair,

I LITERALLY CRIED.

and even started to get along with the other girls.

ISN'T IT WEIRD THAT WE ALL HAVE BANGS?

HA HA!

WHY ARE WE SHOWING THIS? THIS HAPPENED ONCE! FOR LIKE A MINUTE!

Just trying to end on a positive note. Settle down.

Katie had learned a lot, she felt.

She was all "listen:"

LISTEN:

THIS IS WHAT I'VE LEARNED.

THERE ARE THINGS WE CAN'T CHANGE, AND WE JUST HAVE TO ACCEPT THAT.

AND MAYBE THAT'S SOME KIND OF GRACE.

THAT'S YOUR BIG LESSON? THAT'S WHAT YOU JUST FIGURED OUT?

YEAH. WHAT?

GOD GRANT ME THE *Serenity* TO ACCEPT THE THINGS I CANNOT CHANGE **COURAGE** TO CHANGE THE THINGS I *CAN*, AND *WISDOM* TO KNOW THE *Difference*

MY MOM SENT IT TO ME WHEN WE OPENED. I PUT IT UP WHEN SHE VISITED THAT ONE TIME, REMEMBER?

THAT WAS *THREE YEARS AGO*. YOU'VE BEEN STARING AT THIS THING EVERY DAY FOR THREE YEARS.

. . .

GOTTA GO!

And so, life went on. Summer came, and--

OH, STOP. WE GET IT.

Andrew finally moved to the city. Katie wrote him a glowing letter of recommendation.

THANKS, K. REALLY.

I HEAR YOUR NEW BOSS IS A REAL ASSHOLE!

UNLIKE ME...

When Andrew left, Patrick became chef by default.

He asked Hazel out that same afternoon.

I GIVE IT THREE WEEKS.

Katie's restaurant opened, weeks late, way over budget, but it did well, and she was happy there.

IT'S PACKED EVERY NIGHT!

AND YOU'RE DOING THE BEST COOKING OF YOUR LIFE.

It was often said that Lucky's had a real energy to it, that there was something special about it.

UH, YEAH: *MY FOOD,* DUH.

And Katie? She was the same old Katie.

I'M STILL PRETTY YOUNG, BUT THANKS.

Still cooking. Still making people happy.

OR AT LEAST TRYING, EVERY DAY!

...still talking to herself.

320

And for years after she moved out of the little apartment, Katie would drop in a few nights a week to leave bread on the rafters,

but
she
never
saw
another
house
spirit.

Acknowledgments

There would be no *Seconds* without my team of Jason, Nathan, and Dustin, and without the whole team at Random House/ Ballantine. I have been truly blessed to have all of you with me on this book. All love to my friends and family for all their support during these wild and crazy years. Thanks to Mike S. for providing the recipe in chapter 3—not only did he write it, he actually came to my house and cooked it in front of me, and then we ate it. Additional thanks to Joel and Cory, my food and restaurant consultants, and very special thanks to Heather, Julie, Rosanna, Vili, and Miguel, for helping me to not completely destroy my body during this process.

A Note about the Assistants

Jason Fischer (drawing assistant) is a cartoonist from Los Angeles now living in Portland, Oregon. He loves to draw monsters and food. He enjoys collecting rocks, Daruma dolls, knives, pressed pennies, and Playmobil people.

Nathan Fairbairn (color) is a colorist and writer of comics. He's also a pretty decent cook, despite what his kids might tell you. He lives in Vancouver, Canada.

Dustin Harbin (lettering) is a cartoonist who lives and works in Charlotte, North Carolina. He's too fussy to be a good cook but just fussy enough to be an okay baker.

Additional assistance provided by Megan Messina, Hannah Ayoubi, and Jeremy Arambulo. We love them.

About the Author

Bryan Lee O'Malley is the creator of the bestselling Scott Pilgrim graphic novel series, which was adapted into a major motion picture, *Scott Pilgrim vs. the World,* in 2010. He lives in Los Angeles, where he continues to make comics.